The Secret Di
The Secret Di
The Secret Di
The Secret Di
The Secret Di
The Secret Di

The Secret Diary of a SoundCloud Rapper
The Secret Diary of a SoundCloud Rapper
The Secret Diary of a SoundCloud Rapper
The Secret Diary of a SoundCloud Rapper
The Secret Diary of a SoundCloud Rapper
The Secret Diary of a SoundCloud Rapper
The Secret Diary of a SoundCloud Rapper
The Secret Diary of a SoundCloud Rapper
The Secret Diary of a SoundCloud Rapper
The Secret Diary of a SoundCloud Rapper
The Secret Diary of a SoundCloud Rapper
The Secret Diary of a SoundCloud Rapper
The Secret Diary of a SoundCloud Rapper
The Secret Diary of a SoundCloud Rapper
The Secret Diary of a SoundCloud Rapper
The Secret Diary of a SoundCloud Rapper
The Secret Diary of a SoundCloud Rapper
The Secret Diary of a SoundCloud Rapper
The Secret Diary of a SoundCloud Rapper

Requests for permission should be directed to
1111@1111press.com, or mailed to 11:11 Press LLC, 4732
13th Ave S, Minneapolis, MN 55407.

Cover Art by Matthew Revert
Typeset by Mike Corrao

Paperback: 978-1-948687-43-0 (paperback)

Printed in the United States of America

FIRST AMERICAN EDITION

9 8 7 6 5 4 3 2 1

The Secret Diary of a SoundCloud Rapper

Young Stepdad

For Yung Lean

New Year's Resolution: Shoving a turd back up my own butt, then shitting it out again. Or, you know, like maybe getting a black belt in karate.

I watch a hummingbird eat a bug outside my bedroom window and it turns me on. Like if I could physically shrink myself down to miniature size, I might attempt to initiate romantic relations with the bird. Then again, I've had similar thoughts about other egg-laying animals. Maybe I'm sexually attracted to eggs.

You know when you masturbate in the shower? And then you slip and fall and break your arm and your roommate hears you screaming, so they open the bathroom door and call an ambulance and you're rushed to the hospital naked and in excruciating pain, wanting to die of embarrassment but also still, like, slightly orgasming? That's the way my life feels sometimes. Maybe I should get better at showering. I bet there are YouTube tutorials on showering.

Yesterday I bought five plaid shirts at the department store. The shirts were identical except for variations in color. Gray and red, blue and yellow, green and orange. I purchased one of the shirts in a size too large because they did not have the shirt in my size. I knew I would never wear this shirt, but I liked the pattern and I wanted to believe a shirt could be more than something to wear. I wanted the shirt to fulfill a higher function. But the shirt could not rise to the occasion. The shirt let me down. So I took the shirt into the backyard and I dug a hole with my hands. I buried the shirt and I woke up with dirt under my fingernails.

I basically want to go on a rampage and stomp a permanent smile into every skull. I don't smile because I live in a hole. That doesn't mean I don't want you to smile. In the end that's all I want. For you to smile. Then why is it so goddamn hard? This is making me so mad.

When you're ashamed and embarrassed of all the best memories in your life. And how you hate when good things happen to you. You love others so much you want to die for them. For all of them. "Hey, you, I want to die for you." You sick, insidious bastard. All you want is for them to remember you. You want to tattoo the image of your greatness onto their grey matter like it's the American flag. I'm so angry at you and it fucking sucks because I am you.

I'm your goddamn boss so shut up and sit down.

Amazon has become my go-to website for masturbation fantasies. They sell so many varieties of butt plugs, dildos, nipple clamps, mouth gags, crotchless panties, etc. I browse the products, becoming increasingly aroused as I add the items to my shopping cart. I make the fantasy more erotic by only adding items that I could afford, which eliminates expensive BDSM gear and technologically advanced dildos. I read customer reviews, cross-check prices on other websites, and fill my cart with the perfect balance of new and surprising, yet also practical and affordable, sex toys. When I've achieved the perfect balance, I masturbate to my online shopping cart, specifically to the fantasy of the items arriving within a week in a brown Amazon box. After I've orgasmed, I delete the items from my cart and never buy any of them. I believe I've perfected online shopping.

I've been sexually curious for as long as I can remember. When I was six years old, I would look at women in my stepdad's workout magazines. The women in those magazines wore skimpy outfits, revealing tanned and oiled skin, muscles in places I'd never seen muscles, and almost everything on full display. Eventually I discovered his other stash of magazines. I saw the places that were covered up in the muscle magazines, but these women did other things with their bodies. Where the muscle women flexed and posed to demonstrate their power and dominance, the women in these other magazines spread themselves, bent over, begged on their knees. I was attracted and repelled, but as a child I could not distinguish what aspects made me feel one thing and what made me feel the other. Once, my stepdad and his friend locked themselves in the bathroom to look at one of these dirty magazines together. They used to work out together too. These are two unrelated examples of male bonding.

The first person I ever kissed was my sister's best friend. The second person I ever kissed was my best friend. In fifth or sixth grade, some of my friends were sleeping over at my house. At sleepovers, we usually swam, played sports, watched a movie, and talked about girls. That's probably what we did this time too. But as we were all getting into bed, one of our friends starting touching the rest of us, snuggling and cuddling. I guess it felt nice to be touched in that way because pretty soon we were all doing it, pressing our bodies up against each other, moving our hands over each other's warm bodies. That's all we did, and then eventually we fell asleep. In the morning, one of us quietly expressed regret about the previous night. The rest of us shrugged off the experience. We didn't know what we had done or how to process it. Then one night, months later, the friend who had instigated the whole thing was staying the night at my place. My family had moved from a house into an apartment by this time. But one time, before we moved out of our house, I was on the phone with this friend while my mom and stepdad argued. My mom cried out my name and I ran into the living room. My stepdad had my mom's shirt clenched in his fist, holding her as if he was going to strike her with his free hand. I told him to stop and he did. "Did your dad hit your mom?" my friend asked. He asked it so calmly, as if this were a normal thing. I told him no, he didn't. Years later, reflecting on that memory and that friend, I realize he'd probably experienced a lot of similar moments in his house too. But maybe his dad actually did punch his mom. Or maybe, when he tried to stop his dad, his dad went after him instead. Anyway, we were living in an apartment when he stayed over this other time, and he brought up that night when all of us cuddled together. He said that he and one of our friends, whose sister I had kissed the year before, had pursued it further, that it was fun and no big deal. This friend was sort of my best friend, second only to the friend whose sister I had kissed, so I trusted him and what he did next. We kissed and touched each other's young penises, listening to Eminem, in an apartment where I would witness the dissolution of my parents' marriage.

How I came to kiss my best friend's sister was a game of truth or dare, but it was more than a game. I guess we'd had innocent childhood crushes on each other for a year or two. Then one night, sleeping over at my best friend's house, his sister's friend came and got me. She spoke to me privately in another room, told me that my best friend's sister had a crush on me and wanted me to come into her room after my best friend fell asleep. This would be easy enough. My best friend always fell asleep early, sometimes almost immediately after dinner. I was a night owl. I'd often stay awake far later than he did, reading or listening to music or watching a movie or lying in bed, thinking of so many things. So after he fell asleep on this night in February, I went into her room. The friend was staying over, so the two of us weren't alone. They wanted to play a game of truth or dare. Of course, the questions were all targeted and the result was this: we liked each other, agreed to be boyfriend/girlfriend, and we kissed, a quick peck on the lips. Then I went back to my friend's room and fell asleep happy. The next morning, the sister's friend wanted to talk to me in private again. She said the sister regretted what we'd done, and we were no longer boyfriend/girlfriend. That was the end of that and the three of us kept it a secret. But then months later, my other best friend — the one who'd initiated intimate contact between our group of friends — was pressuring me into(?) asking this other girl out. He refused to understand why I didn't(?) like her, this girl who he and another friend of ours had already gone out with ("going out" at this time implied(?) almost nothing, as there was nowhere for us to go and nothing for us to do). Finally, I confessed to him what had happened with our other friend's sister. I told him that we'd kissed and I still liked her and no one else. He spread the news quickly and mercilessly. The sister was so upset that she and I had to talk to the principal at our school about it. She denied anything ever happened. Nobody seemed to believe my side of the story. Or maybe they did. I've never figured that out. My best friend was upset, but he forgave me soon enough, and so did his parents. We moved on with our lives, never speaking of it again that I can recall, except that I believe the sister did eventually admit, at least to a few people, that we kissed. Maybe a year after this incident, I discovered internet pornography.

After downloading celebrity nudes to the desktop of the family computer by accident, I discovered Kazaa or one of the other early piracy platforms. I had no idea what my sexual preferences were or that such a thing as sexual preferences even existed, but the first porn that stuck with me and turned me on in a different way were Heather Harmon's Deep Throat videos. She was a popular amateur porn star who found notoriety and acclaim for her webcam blowjob videos, mostly deep-throating her husband, who remained offscreen (other than his penis, which was almost always entirely inside her mouth) in most of the videos. Some of her videos involved tit-fucking or anal sex, but deep-throating was the predominant activity. Most of the videos were very short. Most ended with her taking a load of semen on her face or tongue. I'd discovered by this point that cumshots were a common, if not inevitable, conclusion to many online porn videos, but I'd never been attracted to that aspect before. If anything, I tried to avoid it by watching mostly lesbian or solo girl porn. But Heather Harmon's confidence and smile, how she always seemed to be in control, transforming degradation into pleasure, turned me on. Years later, as an adult, I found the videos again — and I found they still turned me on. I thought it might be her voice, but I watch most porn on mute. So maybe it's the other stuff I mentioned. Or maybe, in the early 2000s, this woman from the south perfected a subcategory of pornography so well that it permanently etched certain fantasies into my sexual psyche. Not before or after my adolescent discovery of Deep Throat have I ever specifically sought out the work of a porn star. I'm more likely to browse themed Tumblrs and reddit forums. Or, you know, Amazon.

I lost my virginity in the den of my girlfriend's uncle's house. One Saturday, my girlfriend was competing in a forensic debate tournament at a high school across town. Between debates, we walked down to Barnes & Noble and she stole a copy of Baudelaire's *The Flowers of Evil* for me. That was true love at fourteen. She won third place and was awarded a trophy, so after the awards ceremony we bought condoms at a gas station and caught a ride back to her uncle's house. Her aunt and uncle had recently moved in down the street from her parents, but were rarely home due to their work schedules. Looking back, maybe it wasn't an aunt and uncle. Whatever the relation, we were more or less given free rein of the house to fool around. My girlfriend told me she was a virgin too, but later I'd find out that was far from the truth. I can't recall what music we listened to. Probably something goth. I have very few memories of the sex we had, partially because I was also dealing with severe depression and would soon be put on a bad cocktail of antidepressants and antipsychotics, but we seemed to be fucking all the time. This girl believed she was a vampire, occasionally spoke in tongues and other voices, told me she suffered from an incurable and eventually crippling disease, and cheated on me with a girl who a few years later would overdose on heroin, but we dated for around nine months. When we broke up, she gave me a dead goldfish in a plastic easter egg. When that didn't faze me, she told me she was pregnant and that I had to pay for an abortion. I sold some records and a drumset and gave her the money. Then she spent the money on drugs and told her new boyfriend, a crust punk ten years older than me/than her, that I'd given her nothing for her fake abortion. I still have that copy of *The Flowers of Evil.* I wonder if she still has the trophy she won that day.

There was this girl I went to high school with. We both moved out to the coast when we turned eighteen, which is what a lot of people from our town did. In high school, she'd give me hugs and flirt with me even though we shared no mutual friends or common interests. I thought she was attractive and friendly. Out on the coast, we found ourselves hanging out. The first time she came over, we smoked weed and made out. Then she wanted to move to my bedroom, but I didn't have any condoms, so while she got naked in my bed, I drove to the grocery store and bought condoms. I rushed things and got too eager and basically as soon as I had the condom on, not even in bed with her yet, I came. I was embarrassed and didn't know what to do, so I left the room, stood in the hallway and told her

I'd be just a minute. But it must've seemed like I was uncomfortable with the whole thing or something, and it was all massively awkward, so when I got back into bed we just held each other and fell asleep. We hung out a few times after that, but never in that way. We went to the beach once. Another time at her apartment, she told me she was on a diet that consisted exclusively of tuna salad. That's about as close as we ever got. I hope the best for her though. She was always a nice person.

There was this other girl I met on the coast. We sort of dated for a brief time. Things almost worked out well between us, but instead they went terribly. We met partying with a mutual friend and soon it became evident that we liked each other. The first time we hooked up, we went back to my place. There were no sheets on my bed and my feet were black from wandering around in the woods on acid all week. Not long after, when we were hanging out, she'd go take showers with this other guy. I didn't necessarily mind, but it still seems strange to me that in this group of friends, if five or ten of us were hanging out, a few of them would excuse themselves from the party to take a group shower in someone's else's apartment. I've seen her since and she seems to be doing well. She was happy and we looked back fondly on the crazy times we had on the coast. I sort of wish there had been more of those times. I also sort of wish they had never happened.

There are people I will never talk about, either because I hurt them too much or they hurt me too much. You probably feel that way about some people too. What I'm going to do is list their names here, tear out this page and set it on fire. You can do it too. I hope this offering absolves us of the pain we feel and the pain we've dealt.

_____

_____

_____

_____

Now let it burn.

Now do you feel free?

Whether I ever sincerely tried to kill myself, it's hard to say. There was this time, at nineteen, when I swallowed so many Percocets and drank so much vodka. I wasn't depressed or manic at the time. I wasn't trying to get fucked-up either. The goal was obliteration, self-effacement. So yeah, I guess if I never woke up the next morning, you'd say I tried to die. In truth, I wanted an alternative to life and death. I wanted a third choice. And I guess in a way I'm still looking for one. But in the months before this almost-overdose, I had a transformative experience on ayahuasca. I thought I learned something from that, but given my later actions, I guess I learned shit. Or maybe that's what I needed, a return to that ayahuasca state. Whatever the case, I met a good person around this time. We had a good thing going. I stopped destroying myself for a little while. Then I let that good thing die.

A friend's girlfriend's friend's cousin once kicked me out of her apartment for making dead baby jokes. She was sixteen years old and had recently given birth to a beautiful boy. She was right to kick me out of her apartment. I was wrong to make dead baby jokes. I still make dead baby jokes.

I am desperately trying to come to terms with something I cannot identify. It's the UFO inside my heart and mind. It visits when I least desire or expect. Like Mulder, I want to believe. I want to believe I'm a good person. I want to believe I can be an even better person. I want to make a positive impact on the people around me, on my community. I want to think that the people who have known me still have fond memories of the time we spent together. But it's so hard to be good when a motherfucking alien spontaneously rises up inside you, taking over. You do things that you would never do. You say things you would never say. And even though you are not yourself, you are responsible for the actions of this alien inside you. That is why I remain guarded. Don't let people too close.

Don't say too much or too little. Be kind and complimentary. Remain calm no matter the circumstances. Because all the alien needs to take over again is the smallest opening. Then my heart and mind are no longer my own and bad things happen.

If Borges lived in the age of internet porn, his Library of Babel would look so much different. Before going blind, Borges enjoyed the cinema. Sitting in a dark, cavernous room, with a sustained dream projected for a silent, rapt audience, this was a transformative experience for a young Borges. He liked *King Kong*. I believe he would have also found something transformative sitting before a computer in a dark room, alone, selecting from an endless catalog of perverse dreams. I don't know if he would have morally condoned the experience, but I do believe he would contemplate it, and that as a consequence the Library of Babel would be less godlike. The structure would be fleshier, the books on the shelves cruder, uglier, as if created by an extinct and forgotten subset of humanity that never evolved past blind fucking and killing. And if ever you pulled a book from these shelves, you'd turn the pages with a dildo shaped like a fist.

A few months ago, I had to get up off the toilet while in the middle of taking a shit. I don't remember why it was so urgent for me to get up, but I did. I waddled, pants around my ankles, into my bedroom to grab something. This person who came home with me the night before was still asleep. I don't remember their name. Anyway, I got whatever I needed and waddled back to the toilet and finished shitting. A while later, they got out of bed, and they stepped in my shit. There was a nugget of shit on the floor of my bedroom and they stepped in it. I blamed the dog, but they knew I was lying.

Apparently some shit had been stuck to my ass or hadn't fully plopped out and it fell out onto the floor as I waddled into my bedroom. I basically pooped on the floor and then this person I'd met the night before stepped in my poop. The way we laughed about it, I knew I'd always love them. I felt that love again this morning, remembering this happy time. We never saw each other or spoke again after they left my place that morning. God, how I loved them.

Last night, I almost bought a satin hood on Amazon. It was black with only a mouth hole. I liked the idea of it. Plus the hood was only eleven dollars and had mostly positive reviews. I put the satin hood in my shopping cart and masturbated. Afterward, I removed the hood from my shopping cart. I'm still thinking about it a bit.

The earliest nightmare I can recall also happens to be one of my few memories of the time when my parents were still married. I must've been two or three years old. I was sleeping in my parents' bed. They had a waterbed that squished and burbled. The bed frame was heavy and dark. Their room smelled faintly like weed from my dad's blue pipe. One night I was awoken by two prehistoric monsters in the backyard, clawing at the window. One of the monsters had an elephant trunk and gray flesh and tusks. Large hooves and dark eyes. Our black lab, Bucky, tried to fight off the monsters, but the monsters killed him. Then I woke up and my mom made me a peanut butter and jelly sandwich.

I look back on that first nightmare with fondness. Maybe because it's one of the few things I remember about my parents' marriage. Other than a plate being thrown against a wall and getting stung by a wasp. The next round of nightmares, beginning after my mom moved in with my first stepdad, plagued me far worse. I watched a lot of horror movies, so that played an influence, but the worst dreams were totally disconnected from the movies and books I read. The worst of them happened in daylight. We were at my yia-yia's mobile home in a retirement community in Pismo Beach. Standing on the porch with my mom, I watched a tall, human-shaped shadow walk up the steps of a mobile home across the street and go inside. The shadow was fuzzy, almost like television static, and maybe six feet tall. Faceless, impenetrable, but distinctly humanoid. I told my mom to look at the man but she could not see the man. I don't know how long I saw the shadow man for. Maybe a minute. But that was only the first of several encounters.

Back at home, I dreamed of the shadow man. In the first in a sequence of nightmares, the shadow man stalked across our backyard, killed our dog Zito, and broke through our sliding glass back door. My stepdad tried to defend us, but the shadow man killed him as well. Somehow I ended up locked in my room, helpless as the shadow man did unspeakable things to my mom. The shadow man haunted me in dreams for a year or two, until he faded as quickly as he'd arrived in my life.

Fast-forward to me at fourteen, dealing with hormones and an unhealthy relationship, but also the onset of severe depression and troubling spats of hallucinations, paranoia, and anxiety attacks. Right around the time this all started, I awoke one night and an eyeless demon stood over my bed, watching me. The demon had big teeth and gray skin. It looked like one of the Cenobites from Hellraiser. I wasn't panicked. I looked at the demon and thought, "Hey, that's a demon." I was awake for long enough to know it really happened. Then I closed my eyes and went back to sleep. In the morning, I told my mom what had happened. She didn't know what to say or think. I think now of the demon as a harbinger, coming to warn me of the hell I would soon descend into. Maybe I could've avoided all that if I'd listened. And if I could have avoided the pain I experienced, the pain I inflicted, would I go back and change things? My dad now considers those the lost years, but for me they were formative. That period was me processing all the pain I'd taken in but never processed throughout my childhood. Anyway, I'm digressing. The shadow came back, is what I meant to say. The shadow came back in a bad way. I slept with the lights on for a full year because otherwise the shadow man would get me in the dark. He'd be there at the end of dark hallways. Corners, closets…the shadow man lurked everywhere. At night I couldn't bear to be within sight of windows unless there were curtains or blinds. I feared the shadow man would be there, watching me, ready to break inside like he'd done in my dream as a child. I wasn't afraid of death. No, there was something much worse. I still don't know what it is, but I lived with a fear I hope to never feel again. Sometimes, in books, I encounter descriptions and references to something very similar to my shadow man, and I think, I'm not the only one. The shadow man went away entirely after I was prescribed Zyprexa and Wellbutrin, but the combination of pills set off other problems. This resulted in a brief stay at Vista del Mar, a youth psychiatric ward in southern California. Later, back at home, they promptly took me off one of the pills. Sadly, I can't recall which. Eventually, I started not taking the other pill either without telling my parents. It would be another year or more before I became fully human again.

The youth psychiatric ward was a disaster, and not just for me. I self-admitted based on the recommendation of my therapist. He claimed to have been admitted there himself after attempting suicide as a teenager. By that point, my problems were becoming too acute for therapy. He was afraid for me and I was afraid for myself. So my mom and second stepdad drove me down there. Being self-admitted is very casual. I had time to pack books, clothes, and a few other things, although they don't allow you to bring that much in. They were very concerned about my weight. I was extremely frail at that time. The solution for that was to feed me an extra egg salad sandwich every day between mealtimes, along with protein shakes. We each had a private room and they locked us in at night. We spent most of the day in a common room with a television. Aides supervised us. The aides were friendlier and more personable than the doctors. I think they'd yet to get burnt out watching so many ruined lives come and go. All of us patients had very different backgrounds. One girl claimed to be a wiccan and a satanist. I thought she was an idiot. Another guy, maybe a year or two older than me, had a Jack Skellington tattoo. He was in there for shooting a gun at his mom's boyfriend. I never found out why he was trying to kill his mom's boyfriend. During my stay, Jack Skellington and another patient started spending too much time together. Relationships were not condoned, so they were forced to spend time apart. The exercises they'd make us do were mostly useless. Little hour-long workshops where we'd gauge our mental and emotional state based on happy faces and sad faces, like the sliding pain scale doctors use. 1 through 10. Today I am a 1. Today I am a 10. Oh yeah, and one guy there, his eyes were cloudy with blood because he'd hung himself, burst the blood vessels in his eyes, but failed to die. The sessions with actual doctors were ineffectual, impersonal, and extremely brief. They asked surface questions from a list then excused you back to your room or the common area. There was no outside access except for a small concrete patio. You couldn't see the sky because the walls around the patio were so high. The ward was split into two wings, one for male patients and one for female patients, but for most of the day we commingled in the common area. For some reason, they made us switch wings twice during my brief stay. One day, all the boys had to move to the wing where the girls were at and all the girls had to move to the wing where the boys were at. Then a day or two later, they made us repeat. Oh, there was a solitary room too. One guy got stuck in there for freaking out and punching shit. The guy with bloody eyes liked to go in there sometimes too. Other than that, we were mostly all just fine. Just fucked up and in need of help. Help is the last thing most of us would ever find in there.

My recovery from psychological fallout was facilitated by two things: literature and psilocybin mushrooms. Sartre's *Nausea*, Kafka's *The Metamorphosis,* Camus' *The Stranger*, Celine's *Journey to the End of the Night*... books like these were part of the reason I eventually crawled out of the dark pit I'd fallen into. A strong support network of family and friends helped too, but the reality is, when you've gone that far away from yourself, you've already pushed everyone else away. There's no way for other people to reach you when you can't even reach yourself. I needed those books to break the ice, to be human again. But that was only stage one of the process. During this time, I guess a lot of people probably thought I was on drugs all the time. I rarely slept, I was a skeleton, erratic and strange and moody. But I embraced a drug-free lifestyle.

My perspective shifted when I discovered Huston Smith's *Cleansing the Doors of Perception*, a sort of response to Huxley's famous work. I was familiar with Smith's work as a religious scholar, so it surprised me that he'd write seriously on psychedelics, for which he adopted the term entheogen, which better conveyed the substances' validity as spiritual, emotional, and psychological tools while avoiding the stigma of recreational abuse. I read *Cleansing the Doors of Perception* and came away convinced that psilocybin mushrooms would have a positive benefit on me, or at least were something I needed to try. I'd never even smoked weed at this point. A friend acquired two eighths of mushrooms for us and we set out planning our first psilocybin trip together. We decided to take them on a day when school let out early. We drove to Pin Oak Park, where I'd spent summers sweating and dying through football practice. It was winter and the temperature was in the thirties. We ate the mushrooms and sat by a tree. We had a few other friends who had agreed to check in on us, make sure we were fine and didn't need anything. I don't want to go into my experience that day, but it changed my life. Later, after our friends left, I thought I'd come down and could drive my friend and I home. But when we began to drive, the car elongated into a very long vehicle. I couldn't drive a car that long, so I pulled over. We tried again several times before the car returned to its normal shape. In the weeks that followed, my parents all independently made comments about how I seemed happier, like I was enjoying life again. And the truth is, I was. The mushrooms reminded me of everything I'd been missing. Literature helped me realize that I was living in a cage. The mushrooms broke me out of it.

These people one day, they asked if I had any blinds in the house. I told them no, I only have curtains. Technically I have sheets covering all my windows. These people warned me against blinds anyway. "When our first daughter was a year old, she strangled herself to death in the blinds in her room. We thought she was in there playing, but she got trapped in the blinds." They told me this happened last year. They'd lost their first child and the wound was still so fresh. They started to cry. Their beautiful infant lay beside them in its portable carseat, peaceful and small and oblivious to the tragedy that preceded its birth. I told them how sorry I was, but really, how fucking sorry can you be? Sorry doesn't cut it in situations like that. They wept quietly for some time before I walked away, never to see them again. When I think of the worst thing that could happen, I think of those people. I think of the blame and the guilt and the doubt and the sorrow and everything else they must face on a daily basis. What are their private conversations like? And what's so terrible is that they have to march on and try to enjoy life, or at least go through the motions of enjoying it. For their surviving child, for each other, for themselves. If I ever saw them again, I would tell them they were doing a good job. But they were only passing through town.

Sometimes death brings us together, like when my grandfather passed away at his youngest son's wedding. My grandfather's cancer spread rapidly and without remorse, but he held on to the wedding day. He was too sick to even attend the ceremony, which was held in his and my grandmother's back-yard. So he lay in his death bed, listening to the wedding over a baby monitor. Within hours of the vows, he passed away. We were all still in the house. I remember crying, hugging my cousins. That was our grandpa and he was gone. In truth, we'd already lost our first grandpa before any of us were born. My father's father stepped on a landmine in Viet-nam. He left behind a wife and three kids. In return, the government gave them a house and awarded him the Congressional Medal of

Honor. The family was flown out to to meet President Lyndon B. Johnson. There's a photo of my father, a young boy then, wielding a pocket knife in the White House. The knife was a gift from the president.

There's a lot of other people who have died. Ricky overdosed on heroin, alone in his apartment. Margaret was found dead in a desert outside Las Vegas. I can't talk about them all. And even the ones who I can, I just can't.

There's this spot at my left temple, beneath the curly hair of my sideburn. Last summer, the spot began to flake. Sheaths of dead white skin sloughed off. I got obsessed. I dug my fingernail into my scalp, sometimes for an hour at a time, scraping away a seemingly endless amount of skin. Dead skin caked under my nail, powdered my clothes like snow. A few days after the spot appeared, it turned soft and sticky. My skin was perpetually moist there. Raw and tender. I rubbed it like you'd rub a favorite place on a lover's body. Blood started caking up beneath my nail with the dead skin. I knew I should stop touching it and let the spot heal, but I grew attached to it. This little wound became a sort of friend. Eventually it healed, but it comes around again every few months and we restart our routine, picking up where we left off like old friends.

The period in my life when I believed tube worms lived in the flesh around my genitals was a serious low point. The period in my life when I thought I had an STI because I was scrubbing my asshole too much with Irish Spring soap was another low point, but not as low as the tube worms. A high point is right now, watching a pigeon on the rail of a third floor balcony trying to eat snow. It's snowing and I like myself again. Why did I ever stop liking myself?

For my entire adult life, I've been convinced that I carry with me a dormant disease that will eventually destroy my body and mind. I've had visions of myself in hospital beds. But then again, I'm also convinced I'll die in a car crash. I squirm when I think of myself trapped in a ruined steel cage, slowly bleeding to death as rescuers attempt to pry me from the wreckage. For me, the idea of being trapped is worse than death. I'd rather step on a steel bear trap. At least then I could do what foxes do and chew my own leg off. In reality, my teeth are hardly equipped to chew steak. Just ask the friend who had to perform the Heimlich on me several years ago.

My teeth. I've had three oral surgeries in three years. Braces twice. Extractions, root canals, emergency procedures, and I'm going on almost a decade of chronic pain that might be a symptom of TMJ and might be psychosomatic. I'm not complaining. By now I've learned to distance myself from the claustrophobic panic that grips me in the dentists' chair. I've acquired an appreciation of the fine work of professionals in the dentistry field. But the time Jim punched me in the mouth, shattering my maryland bridge, fracturing my jaw, and knocking my front tooth back five millimeters, that really tops them all. After a night of drinking, we decided to turn things up a notch. Instead of heading home, we headed to another bar. On our walk there, we somehow started punching our friend Garrett in the stomach. Garrett's gut is a source of fascination. He's able to flex it into an impenetrable pot. I laid into him with body shots and he didn't blink. Then Jim tried, but Jim had never learned to throw a punch. His movement was more like someone lashing at a canvas with a paintbrush, which makes sense. Jim is an artist. I wasn't a fighter, but I'd done a little boxing training with my second stepfather at the Police Activities League. I'd spent even more time shadowboxing and hitting the heavy bag at home. And because I am a nerd, I'd read a few books on the basics of boxing. So I told Jim I'd teach him how to throw a punch. I said he might someday need to defend his family from monsters or the enemy or something. We were drunk. I could've said anything. This whole time, our other friend, Jeff, pleaded with us to stop. This is the one occasion where Jeff was the source of reason. We got a round of shots at the next bar and carried on our antics on the smoking patio. Jim was getting the mechanics of a punch. I wanted to put it into action, so I told him to hit me as hard as he could in the stomach. And he did. He hit me as hard as he could, only he missed my stomach by a wide margin. His knuckles connected beautifully with my mouth causing extreme physical trauma and bloodying his hand. Garrett found the fake tooth from my broken bridge and asked if he could swallow it. I told him sure, why not, so he did. As I tried to remain calm and assess the damage, my intern at the time approached me. Turns out he'd spotted me enter the bar and wanted to introduce me to a friend of his. But haha! My mouth was mangled. I looked up the emergency number of my dentist, but the first four times I dialed the number, I reached the cellphone of the landlord of a recording studio space I was looking into at the time. I was drunk enough and riding the highs of an adrenaline rush — he had to explain who he was and that he had no affiliation with my dentist. No matter how hard I concentrated on my dentist's emergency number, I kept calling him back. Eventually, I succeeded in reaching my dentist, but it was almost two in the morning and my frequent calls woke her up. "Are you drunk?" she asked. "A little," I said. I wasn't in a state to convey the severity of the damage and she could tell. She told me to go home, which is exactly what I was afraid of.

The best kisses are the ones where we lick each other's teeth.

We shot frogs. Dozens or hundreds of frogs. My father took me out to the Kern River and we stalked the banks, shooting tiny frogs at point blank range with pellet guns. Another time, we drove out to the countryside to shoot tarantulas. My father told me that at the right time of year, thousands of tarantulas swarmed the desert. We were going to gun them down. I shot a beaver in the head once. I would've made it into a hat but we couldn't retrieve its body. We shot birds. But most of all, I remember the frogs, their corpses. I was just a boy. My father, he regrets it now. I don't know where that killing spirit came from, what possessed us to do it. What I do know is that a lot of people on this planet carry that bloodlust with them every day. The need to control, to maim, to collect, to permanently alter the life status of another living organism, is not distinctly human. Cats play with their prey. Dogs kill without knowing why. But we should know better. We have to know better and we have to be better.

I read a summary of a scientific survey that described dire effects ocean acidification is having on the shell of some type of snail integral to the ocean's food chain. Lots of smaller fish eat these snails, and the smaller fish are in turn eaten by salmon and other larger fish. With the snails in decline, the prey fish are thinning out. In turn, coho salmon seem to be hunting deeper, putting them in direct competition with chinook salmon for an already declining food source. This is all conjecture, but it's based on the limited scientific information available. All I know is that if the oceans die, so will we.

Today I want to design a multi-course meal inspired by the diet of whales. For a first course, I'll have a krill salad. Then we'll move on to squid ink pasta, shrimp skewers, and salmon nigiri. Sea lion steaks will be served as the main dish. For dessert, we have the imminent death of all life on this planet except whales. For it is the era when whales grow legs and walk out of the ocean, marching over our corpses to occupy the wastelands we've left for them. But the wisdom of the whale people will let them repair the mess we've made of this planet. They are the rightful heirs, and their reign will be good.

Sometimes, browsing Amazon, I see the butt plugs with furry animal tails attached. I think of buying one even though that sort of play does nothing for me. It seems like something I should try anyway. Like, what if I did a challenge where for an entire year I could only engage sexually in ways and with devices that held no appeal to me? Would I discover new things we liked? Maybe some. I'd probably meet some new kinds of people. Which reminds me. There's this porn I want to make with someone, if I ever meet the right person, like maybe someone I'd marry. In the porn, the woman I marry is wearing a Ronald Reagan mask and otherwise naked. I'm fucking her in the ass and the camera is POV style, so the audience can only see Reagan. "California Uber Alles" by the Dead Kennedys is the soundtrack. It seems kind of dumb now that I've written it down. I don't know.

I'm not what you'd call a pants shitter, but there were a few times early in my life when I shit my pants. One time I was surf fishing with my dad on the California coast. We were catching fish, but I also had a deep need to shit. So he told me to walk up the beach and shit in the sand. But I wasn't great at squatting. I pulled down my swim trunks and started doing my business. But I was squatting all wrong and the shit was just going into my swim trunks. I was shitting on my own pants and by the time I realized this, it was too late. There were miles of endless sand and I was a small boy, but somehow I managed to shit all over myself. I took off my shorts and went out into the surf to tell my dad. He didn't even get mad. He walked up the beach, got my shorts, took them back to the ocean, washed them clean of shit, and gave them back to me. He never scolded me or made fun of me or really even said anything. He just went back to fishing, and we went back to having a good time. I think that experience informs a lot of how I live my life. Don't let shitting on yourself ruin your good time.

The other time I shit my pants was at the end-of-year party when I was in fifth grade. My best friends and I were waiting our turn for the bounce house. Finally our turn came up and we all piled into the bounce house, but as I was climbing in, a turd slipped out of my butt. If I'd shit my pants after the bounce house, that'd be one thing. This was worse. This happened as I was climbing in. If I ran out, my friends would know something happened. So I played it cool and pretended like I hadn't shit my pants. I was wearing loose-fitting gym shorts, so the possibility of shit coming out of my pants was real. I jumped and bounced as if I didn't have pants full of shit, though maybe I was a little more cautious than usual. I still did the butt-bounces that are so fun in bounce houses. And in the end, everything was fine. After our time in the bounce house ended, I went to the bathroom and cleaned up the shit as best I could. Then I went about my day, shitty pants and all.

One of my friends in the bounce house told a funny story once. The story is what I remember him best for, except for his uncanny obsession with golf. A group of us were having a sleepover at his house and, well into the night after his parents had gone to bed, we started talking truth about girls and telling each other raunchy stories. So this friend, whose parents forbid him from seeing PG-13 movies, he starts telling us about this guy. Like most stories, there was a guy, and this guy had a mission. He wanted his girlfriend to suck his dick sideways, like his dick's on his hip. So he tells his girlfriend, "Suck me sideways." And she does. She sucks his dick so hard that his dick shifts positions, permanently moving to one of his hips. So now he's got nothing in front like a Barbie doll and his dick's sideways.

He was sucked sideways and lived happily ever after. I still don't know where my friend heard that story. My guess is that it was a personal fantasy. I believe kinks start young.

Some of my friends in high school used to cut slits in their mattresses, fill a ziplock bag with petroleum jelly or something, and stuff the bag into the slit, then fuck their bed. I never got into bed fucking. Now they sell those fleshy tubes that are supposed to replicate the feel of a pussy or asshole or mouth. I've never used one of those tubes because they don't appeal to me in the same way bed-fucking never appealed to me. I've also heard of teenage boys fucking dogs. The earth is overpopulated, but our desire for sweet fucking remains insatiable. Imagine if babies were born from these communions. There'd be half-human/half-dog babies, half-human/half-bed babies, and eventually, when a half-human/half-dog fucks a half-human/half-bed, there'd be a human/dog/bed hybrid.

Imagine a planet populated by creatures with human heads, dog legs, and mattress bodies. Can we get someone to make that happen?

My spiritual beliefs are none. Even atheism makes me bristle, with its self-assuredness and smugness. Most religions have been exploited as a tool to control the populace, to justify wars and a whole bunch of evil shit. But I'm not totally against religion either. If it works for you, great. Just shut the fuck up about it. I guess that's why I never talk about spirituality with people, except maybe with a few close friends. I believe nothing whatsoever and it's my responsibility to shut the fuck up about it.

But I did not always harbor an absence of beliefs. I was baptized Catholic. I remember attending Catholic church, walking up in front of everyone, sitting down, and picking my nose. My mother was too embarrassed to come get me, so she let me stay up there, picking my nose and eating boogers while I stared at all the praying people. I remember drawing pictures of God with my friend Kevin. God was stoic and old with a long beard. Why is that naturally a child's version of the Catholic God? How did that image get implanted in our brains? Eventually I started going to a Christian church because my best friend and his family switched over. The Christian youth group was different, more informal. They played rock music and a few overnight trips a year where we went up to the mountains, stayed in cabins. We snowboarded, ice skated, and flirted with girls in between prayer sessions. I started dating a girl at one of these things. I was in like seventh or eighth grade at the time.

Then, just as suddenly, I stopped believing. Looking back, it seems so strange that I spent a portion of my life praying every night. I mean, I've got nothing against prayer. I don't know. Maybe I just started putting it all down on paper.

There's another story about my teeth. Since I'm missing two front teeth, never growing the adult set because neither of my parents had theirs either, I had to find replacements. Implants were the natural option. My dentist referred me to an oral surgeon. The oral surgeon made the argument that because I never had the adult teeth, my jaw did not have enough bone to support the teeth, and the implants would fail. He argued that a maryland bridge, a more temporary measure, would be a sounder option considering the history of my mouth. This sounded like sound logic to me, so he went ahead and installed a maryland bridge, shaving down the backs of my two front teeth to build the bridge across the top four. It was the closest I'd ever come to a complete mouth. But when my dentist saw the bridge, he lost his mind. He called the oral surgeon on the phone and screamed at him. Every dentist I saw from then on questioned the bridge. Why did I have it? What an awful thing to do. The overriding belief was that the oral surgeon had made a bad judgment call and consequently screwed me over. Well, a few years ago I learned that the oral surgeon had gone under trial in the early nineties for the murder of his wife. She mysteriously drowned in their bathtub. He was found not guilty, so whatever. Innocent people go on trial all the time. But then something else happened. The oral surgeon shot himself in his office one night. His medical license had been suspended and he was under investigation due to numerous malpractice claims. He committed suicide over the things he'd done to people like me. I wonder if he felt guilty, or if he was only scared for himself. Not all ruined men are alike.

Anyway, more time passed, and the implant I got eventually began to fail. I developed an open white sore that oozed pus. It would grow and grow and grow above the implant like a big fat pimple. Eventually the pressure got so great I'd pop it, splattering the mirror with festering debris. Rubbing whiskey on it helped a little, on the nights when the pain got too extreme. I was afraid, so eventually I went to see a dentist. He told me I should go back to the oral surgeon who'd installed the implant, but their office wouldn't see me because I'd gone to this other dentist to have a look at me. There was a weird reasoning behind this. I was stuck for several months, in perpetual pain, afraid that the infection might be spreading to my brain. My right eye developed a twitch that has never gone away. Whenever I say or do something inexplicable, I wonder if the infection resides even though I received a bone graft and underwent additional surgery to clean out the infection. To be totally honest, I like going under sedation. I love the nothing-state of it. You fall entirely out of time and space, more so than when you're sleeping or pass out. But during that last surgery, I began to dream. I'm not sure if you're supposed to do that. I dreamed that I was holding a large brown beetle, cradling it in my arms. I was petting the beetle like it was a cat. Where art thou, oh beloved beetle?

Ghosts have haunted almost every member of my family. Most will never talk about it, unless times turn desperate. Then we turn to the ghosts for answers. When my problems hit their darkest point, my father sat me down one night to figure it all out. I told him what was happening. Instead of calling me crazy — he seemed to fundamentally disbelieve that mental illness was a thing like physical illness — he told me how when he was a young boy he awoke one night to see his father sitting at the edge of his bed. This would not be totally strange, except that his father had died in Vietnam. That was the first and only time my father ever told me about seeing his father's ghost. At the time, the conversation helped a little. Over time, it helped a lot.

My mother once witnessed the ghost of an alligator cross the street outside her family's Chicago apartment. While working as an engineer on the atomic bomb project in Los Alamos, my great grandfather had a vision of the totality of Planet Earth's history printed on a single scroll. The scroll was made up of bright and vivid colors, except for the very end, which mostly consisted of a black box framing a demonic face. At first it looked like some sort of coincidence, like the creator of the scroll had let a vial of ink spill all over the scroll and it just happened to bleed into something facelike. But as he looked closer, he realized that the demon in the box was the totality of human history. Shortly after he experienced this vision, he quit the atomic bomb project. We're all part of the demon,

but whether we choose to embrace or com-
bat our nature, that part is left up to us.

Years back in my lineage, you will find witch doctors, saints, and shapeshifters. One of my descendants on my father's side transformed into a fish at the end of her life. Either that or she walked into the ocean and drowned herself. I have not heard all the secrets, but I have heard rumor of them.

I once came across a home videotape in a thrift shop marked "Hauntings." The tape was only fifty cents, so I bought it out of curiosity. I mostly fast-forwarded over the first thirty or forty minutes, which consisted of two self-proclaimed ghost hunters wandering through dark, abandoned houses with headlamps and EKG meters. The most frightening thing they encountered was a dead cat being eaten by some very large rats. Disgusting, but a far cry from haunting. Then, toward the end of the tape, one of their pointless wanderings cut out. On my first viewing, I believed this to be the end of the tape, until a new image filled the screen. We were in a basement, and the two ghost hunters were standing over a body lying on the table. The body was bloated and bruised. I must have been thirteen or fourteen at the time and the only dead body I'd seen was my grandfather's, when he passed away at my uncle's wedding, so I didn't know how to analytically process a dead body. I mean, it was a corpse. One of the ghost hunters began to cut into the neck of the corpse with a large knife. He cut the head off the corpse and the video ended. This haunted me every night for a while, but I don't think about it much anymore. I guess I never figured out what it means. That no longer seems to bother me.

The worst nightmare I ever had involved a troll stalking me across the living room of my father's house. I tried to escape but all the doors were locked, or the doorknobs turned and turned. The troll lumbered slowly toward me, a knife held in its right hand. I awoke terrified moments before the troll got me. The thing is, I wasn't afraid to be stabbed or mauled. What the troll was going to do to me was far worse than that. And I still believe to this day that if I'd died in that dream, I would've died in real life.

Imagine if a ghost lived in your butt. Would you feel it as a mass, something filling you, or would its presence be more ethereal, manifesting itself as a need to feel filled? What if dildos were alive and ghosts were real and a dildo died inside your butt? Would you orgasm on all that haunt?

Another haunting: Waking up each morning, wondering why I'm still alive. I thought I'd made an agreement with myself to be dead by now. I'm not sad or impatient. I just feel like I've seen how this all plays out. Then again, there's nothing like getting your bare ass spanked on stage in a strip club. They even lit my ass hairs on fire. One guy retracted his dollar bill on the rail for that one, but I'm sure they made a few dollars more.

Today I ate half a three meat sub sandwich for breakfast, macaroni and cheese for lunch, and a pulled pork sandwich for dinner. I looked at the kiwis and bananas in the fruit basket and considered eating some fruit, but I didn't eat any fruit today. Usually I eat some fruit. I don't know. I was into the idea of eating fruit, but I couldn't bring myself to do it. I drank soda water, coffee, and beer.

Something happened in the past year or two where I have a hard time saying what I mean to say. Instead I say things I don't mean. Or I say nothing at all. It's funny how this has happened because I deliberate more than ever over my word selection. I think that's the thing though. I'm so deeply afraid of something and I've grown sick of words. I'd almost rather live in a world where I never speak at all but connect and communicate through body language and sound. That would be a terrible thing, but it's my perfect terrible thing. Except, as sick as I am of words, I need them. I just need to learn how to use them again.

The lowest moments in my life would have marked the end of most lives. I am either stronger or weaker than everyone else. I choose to believe I am stronger. My tendency to slip back into dark moods suggests I might be wrong.

Ricky finally killed himself upon his third suicide attempt. I never understood why he was so hellbent on dying. I mean, I get it. But man, could he play the guitar. He was a good person and at one point a good friend. But even as a person going through so much pain myself, I completely failed to recognize all the pain Ricky was going through. Even after I heard about his first suicide attempt, I thought it must've been an accident or something. Now, looking back, I see how lonesome he really was. I wish I would have called him one last time and told him, "You'll find the perfect girl someday. Just hang on. Don't lose hope." I wish I would have said anything at all to him. I can't remember the last time we talked or hung out. Even though I thought of him, I didn't act on it. There's probably not anything anyone could have said or done to keep him around, but still, I want him to know that his smile and his laugh and his ability to shred were incredible. He was a loyal friend with a steady mind. I wish he wasn't gone.

I come up from the basement, where I record all my shit. I turn on the porch light and step outside to smoke a cigarette. It's snowing out. The light reflects off the snow and everything is beautiful and glimmering. The moon is full and everything is quiet. It occurs to me that apparently no one has stopped by to check on me. I've likely missed work. I walk out into the yard and lie down in the snow. I wave my arms and legs, making a snow angel. But then I notice a smell. There's dog shit beneath the snow. I've smeared it all over. So I make an angel out of dog shit. It's what I do best.

Winter this year is kind of a drag.

Death is a hot topic in America.

I'm not singing this is me drowning.

A one-way plane ticket to anywhere but this life

It's not the body that you want but it's the body that you'll have to wear

Never forgiving others for things you do yourself

Persecuting yourself for crimes others have committed

Making all big life decisions at once and then facing the consequences of them

So lonely your shadow won't hug you back

Seeing the emergency room as an excuse to connect with other humans on an intimate level

All intimate connections are based on

need and nurtured by fear and doubt.

If there was a huge light switch on the side of the planet, I would switch it off

Who turned the lights out on the world?

I did, fuckers.

Scared of your own pets.

I mean, what if they take after you?

When asked about your five year plans during a job interview, respond with a monotone voice, "I want to be a monster."

This is what they want to hear.

This will get the job.

I would describe my attitude toward life as 'slutty.'

In several ways I've devolved over the past year. It's so strange how I shut everyone out. I don't know why I do it. Or how. I love people. Really.

You love everyone but at the same time, you love no one but yourself. Your skepticism in belief is an insane need to be right. You've never been the strongest proponent on any issue. You believe in nothing, firmly. You so deeply believe in nothing that when you discovered an entire field dedicated to it, you turned away from it. You renounce everything by being nothing. You canker sore of a human, you.

All you want to do is create music, or something, anything, that people love more than life itself, but it's hard when you're so sad.

You develop sexual fetishes to appear more interesting. Like that time you wouldn't stop talking about camel slide videos for a month to anyone who would listen and anyone who wouldn't. You were seriously not that into camel slides, dude.

The internet is the great equalizer. Humans will finally shed their bodies and leave this earth, freeing the earth to heal its wounds after centuries of despair.

I'm the type of person who likes nice things but is afraid to admit it, so I break everything a little bit to prove something of its worth.

If I gave you a walnut for your birthday, would you understand that I was trying to say I want to be trees in our next life, or would you say I was an idiot? A sweet idiot. That's all I've ever wanted to be.

Basically, I'm telling you my story backwards, starting at the end and working toward the beginning. The funny thing is, it's not even my story.

If you worry that you're demon possessed, ask yourself what you did to be so lucky.

The closer I get to the truth about myself, the more I want to get away.

You can't seem to understand how afraid I am. That I've been this way for a long time, but not forever. But eventually I'm going to break myself out. I might need a little help.

Hi, my name is _____. I'm a sex addict, a drug addict, a rapper, and I hate the human race. I like to fuck and get fucked up. But I'm totally down to chill also.

Hold up one second. This isn't me at all.

Hey there, I have heavy feelings. I have a past, a portfolio of accomplishments, and enriching life experiences. I understand the art of the personal narrative enough to manipulate people. Not that I'm an expert, but I've been trained by some of the best. My main thing is I'm constantly trying to run away from myself. I have a history of success, but it all feels like failure right now. I need to get back on my feet.

It's funny how I finally recognized how I ruined everything. Now I've got a chance to fix it. Will I make it all better, or will I blow it?

A depression you can chew on. A depression you can savor.

I take myself as seriously as I take junk mail, which is to say tremendously. Who are these people and what do they want from me? Which is the same question I ask about my- self.

Honey, I miss you so much I'd fuck two heads of lettuce and pretend they were your titties. I mean, if lettuce was on sale, I'd do it.

As things stand, I've never gotten as much distance on my ejaculation as I've wanted to. I'm more of a cannonball guy.

I'd be cool with living in a trash can. All my favorite things end up there.

Sometimes I wonder how I got so lucky.

I contradict the demands I impose on myself so often that it's like I'm stuck on a glitchy, frozen NES screen, Mario and Bowser always getting at each other but never getting to each other, forever. That's God and me.

I'm doing what I do because I'm not doing what I'm supposed to do.

I want to stick my hands in a deep fryer then run around shouting, "Who wants chicken fingers?" And if nobody wants chicken fingers, I'll eat them myself and immediately feeling guilty for eating too much.

I'm on some next level shit. Riding dirty on my own grave. Here's the key to my love: don't hurt me. Now here's the secret to me: everything hurts me. I'm like anti-invincible.

I believe in burning bridges when there's no good use for them. We should take a vote to see who's more worthless.

When thinking fondly of others becomes a sickness.

Buy yourself a BB gun and shoot it fast at far targets, hitting none of them but feeling swell.

We now witness the birth of a hideous creature. Oh wait, you're just looking at yourself in the mirror.

It's like everyone I've ever known is screaming at me all at once. I hear you. The problem is I hear everyone else as well.

If sleeping were a pro sport, I would fail miserably and stand no chance at competing, but I would pay to attend matches. "Well boys, this cutthroat match is heading into double overtime. And gosh it's another nailbiter." Hell yeah. Sports and shit.

Sleeping is a team sport.

A world where everyone changes gender every four years, just to keep things in perspective. Being all the genders, one by one by one by one by one by one by one by one by one by one. Until you're dead.

Kicking myself for letting something so small and stupid ruin my life.

Still never snorted a line of coke off a fat titty. My old bandmate told me I hadn't lived until I did. It's basically the first thing I plan on doing after getting a black belt in karate. Maybe next year.

We gotta break on through to the next level of our lives. That means hunting deer and wearing only deer skin clothes, eating only deer meat forever. We can't waste our days high and humping. We've got to get out and fucking kill some shit.

I want a dildo made of antler bone. Even better, imagine if the deer's ghost came out of the antler and licked your butthole? What if you liked it?

Next time we sleep together, let's emulate plants. When I wiggle my fingers like rustling leaves, it means I'm ready to fill you up with chlorophyll. That is how plants make baby plants, right? I wonder if plant birth is painful. This is how I masturbate on acid.

I'd give up so much just to get it all back, but it's too late. For so long I failed to make happiness a priority. Now look where I ended up.

I sit down and write a letter to the boy I used to be.

ABOUT THE AUTHOR

Young Stepdad is a performance artist living somewhere in the United States.

11:11 Press is an American independent literary publisher based in Minneapolis, MN. Founded in 2018, 11:11 publishes innovative literature of all forms and varieties. We believe in the freedom of artistic expression, the realization of creative potential, and the transcendental power of stories.

Lightning Source UK Ltd.
Milton Keynes UK
UKHW010628060621
384987UK00001B/61